Just Clues

Experiences in Reading Comprehension

Grades 2-4

Rosemary Lee Potter   Charles E. Hannemann

Creative Publications
P. O. Box 10328, Palo Alto, CA 94303

Designer: Ed Almazol
Illustrator: Tim Mitoma
Editor: Shirley Hoogeboom

Disclaimer: In this book, all people and places named and events described are fictional.

© 1985 Creative Publications
P.O. Box 10328
Palo Alto, California 94303
Printed in U.S.A.

ISBN: 0-88488-272-1

45678910.8987

Contents

Notes about the Authors

Rosemary Lee Potter (Ed.D.) is a reading specialist at Safety Harbor Middle School with the Pinellas County Schools, Clearwater, Florida. She has been a classroom teacher for 23 years. Dr. Potter has also authored a college textbook, a variety of television-related reading materials, and a syndicated newspaper column. She is a frequent lecturer and consultant in the field of education.

Charles E. Hannemann (Ph.D.) is an Associate Professor of Education at the University of Miami, Florida. He teaches graduate and undergraduate courses in social studies education, and serves as Coordinator of the Area of Instructional Technology. He has authored television-related materials and articles in professional journals.

For more than a decade, Drs. Potter and Hannemann have been developing instructional materials based on the concept now presented in *Just Clues: Experiences in Reading Comprehension*. For example, they co-authored a pioneer article on clue reading entitled, "Conscious Comprehension: Reality Reading Through Artifacts," published in the March 1977 issue of *The Reading Teacher*.

Notes from the Authors

Rationale

For too long, we classroom teachers have **talked** about reading comprehension skills. We have often asked our students to practice higher-order thinking, while not always demonstrating complete awareness ourselves of the specific reading skills and how they may be applied to everyday situations. We have often relied on repetitive workbook practice exercises to teach reading comprehension skills, rather than relying on specific procedures which aid students in the identification, trial, and application of those skills. As a result, students all too often are unable to decide which skill to apply to answer a question or solve a problem. They also find it difficult to transfer skills from use on exercise pages to use in real-life situations.

Here seems to be a paradox. Human beings must make sense of (comprehend) their world through reading real things in their environment: letters, notes, menus, lists, brochures, documents, and more. In other words, in addition to the mandated need for teaching reading comprehension of the printed stories in books, we educators have a real obligation to provide classroom reading experiences that facilitate students' understanding of reading skills and how to apply them every day. *Just Clues* is a discovery approach to reading comprehension that accomplishes just that.

What Is *Just Clues*?

Just Clues is a collection of unique, directed supplementary reading comprehension experiences for students in grades two through four. It provides clues in both print and picture form to motivate and challenge youngsters to read and to create stories. As students handle, examine, and analyze the clues, they use six important reading comprehension skills: specific details; classification; inference; sequence; cause and effect; and main idea. Youngsters find *Just Clues* learning experiences irresistible.

How Does *Just Clues* Work?

When you visit someone's home for the first time, you cannot help but receive impressions about the owner's interests and lifestyle from your observations. For example, many books on a shelf, all related to a single topic, may cause you to conclude that someone in the home has a deep interest in that topic. Notes fastened on the refrigerator door may suggest a very active and responsible family. Numerous family photographs on the wall might suggest close family ties. The more observations you make, the more you comprehend about the family living in the house. With enough observations, you could begin to construct stories about the family.

In the same manner that you would observe clues and construct a story about the family, your students will use the clues in the *Just Clues* experiences. *Just Clues* has been designed to provide students with sets of clues—print and picture items—which, when closely examined and read, will challenge them to create a story. The skills needed to construct the story are the six major reading comprehension skills named above, the ones you are teaching every day. Students want to make up stories and must use the skills with the clues to do so.

Suggestions for Using *Just Clues*

Getting Ready

In this book there are sets of materials for eight experiences. Each set consists of a story guide and a group of clues. The eight story guides, which are designed to be used primarily by the teacher, are found on pages 1–24. The clues, which will be used mainly by the students, are found on pages 27–88 (see Index to Clues on page 25).

We recommend that you prepare the clues for all eight experiences at one time. Tear out the perforated sheets of clues and reproduce them, so that you will have backup copies or additional copies for use with a large group of students. Then cut out the clue items. Note that the back of each clue item is labeled with the title of the story to which the item belongs. Place the clues for each story in a folder, bag, or large envelope, and label the container with the story title. The clues need not be stored in any special order.

You may wish to create a read-along audiotape of the clues and/or Check-up Questions. It may add support for some readers or allow for greater independence.

The eight stories may be used in any order that is appropriate to your students' current interests, needs, and studies. When you have selected the story you wish to use, you will want to read the story guide and all of the clues before presenting the clues to the students.

Grouping Students

Just Clues can be used successfully in a number of different groupings and settings. It should be used initially as a directed learning experience, however, whether the group be an entire class or a single reading group. Later, after students have used one or more stories under teacher guidance, they may want to tackle one of the experiences independently or as part of a small group working together in a learning center. Other situations in which you can use *Just Clues* include the following:
- As an introductory exercise in inquiry/problem-solving
- As a skill prescription in reading comprehension
- As an instructional component within a system's reading program
- As a content area component within interdisciplinary studies
- As a strategy to be used as part of time-out or counseling procedures

Presenting Vocabulary

For each story, lists of Key Words and Supporting Words are given. Some of these words may be difficult because they are unique to a specialized field such as animal husbandry or fund-raising. *Just Clues* experiences often motivate students to attack long and unfamiliar words because they realize that the words are keys with which to unlock the meaning of the story. For example, the word *congratulations* is crucial to the story in which it is used. Substituting another word or words for it would destroy the realism of the clues. The fact remains, then, that some words in these stories, especially the Key Words, deserve special attention and study by the students with the teacher's help. This study may be accomplished in several ways:

1. Since students want to examine the clues as soon as they encounter them, briefly pronounce and discuss any difficult word as it is seen in context. This procedure keeps the thinking and discussion flowing without long interruptions. Words are also learned as needed.

2. Present vocabulary prior to introduction of the clues and before the students begin to examine them. Review pronunciations and meanings of words as you have often done.

3. Combine the two options above to maximize the learning of words. This flexibility allows you to individualize vocabulary instruction, tailoring it to your students' needs.

Presenting the Clues

Hand out the clues to the students. Explain that the clues must be read and examined closely. Tell them that the experience is a little like finding a bottle with a note in it on the beach, and trying to figure out who wrote it and where it came from. Let them know that the items may be examined in any order.

Explain that the various clues go together in some way to make a story. Tell them that it is okay for them to make guesses, as long as they make their guesses based on what they find in the clues. Initial guesses from students might include comments such as, "I'll bet that boy did the drawing"; "I think they are going to run anyway"; or "This story is about raccoons, isn't it?"

Guiding the Discussion

After giving the clues and instructions to the students, allow time for them to examine and read the clues. During this time, students should be encouraged to share the clues, pass them around, and read as many as possible. They will begin to get an idea of the storyline almost at once. However, it will not be fully developed until a thorough discussion has taken place.

Use the seven Discussion Questions provided in the Story Guide for the selected story. Use the questions in the order in which they are presented. For example, always begin with question 1: *Tell me about the clues you have.* Continue with the questions, stopping for discussion where needed. As you ask a question, tell the students what kind of reading skill it will take for them to answer it. If necessary, explain the skill at that point and then repeat the question and move on. For example, when you come to the question that asks students to arrange the clues in the order in which the events seem to have happened, you would say, "You will need to use sequence to answer this question." If students do not understand what you mean by the term *sequence*, explain it with a simple example and then ask the question again. It may be necessary to work through the answer with them, but do not give them your own idea of the sequence of clues. Also remember that, as in real life, some clues may represent events taking place at or about the same time rather than before or after other events.

If at a later time you provide a clues story for independent study, be sure to give the students involved a copy of the seven discussion questions for that story.

Using the Check-up Questions

Six Check-up Questions are included for each clues story. The questions are in multiple-choice format. Each question requires the use of one reading comprehension skill. Students may have to look at the clues again in order to answer these questions accurately. Students may also learn by doing the check-up questions together. Therefore, this activity is intended as a practice review rather than as a test of skill mastery, and as such should not be graded. *Just Clues* is designed to provide stimulating instruction rather than a test of skill mastery. You will want to test complete achievement of skills with other instruments prescribed by your school system.

You may wish to use a recording sheet, however, to indicate a student's practice of the skills and progress toward mastery of them. (A blackline master of a recording sheet is given on page viii.) The recording sheet will enable you to see at a glance which students need more practice with particular comprehension skills, especially if you use both the discussion session and the check-up questions as your sources of information for recording.

Extending the Experiences with Follow-up Activities

Included for each clues story are four follow-up activities which extend the use of the experience to a variety of other reading and language arts skills. For example, after discussing a clues story in depth, students may be asked to role-play a part of the story that is of particular interest, to write a story or poem about situations similar to those experienced by the story characters, or to look up additional information on a topic related to the story. In any case, it is not necessary to have students do all of the follow-up activities or to do the activities in any particular order. Follow-up is often a perfect opportunity to individualize instruction or to provide independent study. Students may wish to refer to the clues already examined as they engage in follow-up experiences.

Extending the Experiences with Related Books

Included for each clues story is a brief list of Related Books which you may wish to obtain for your room library. These books may be used for leisure reading, for book reports, for obtaining additional information, or for piquing students' interest in reading more about topics and situations in the clues stories. Among the books recommended are some which children can read by themselves and others which are better read aloud to the class by the teacher. Every one of the books, however, can be a source of lively discussion relating to the *Just Clues* story.

Record of Progress Name:

COMPREHENSION SKILLS

CLUES STORY	Specific Details	Classification	Inference	Sequence	Cause and Effect	Main Idea
Going Away						
The New Boy						
Just You and Me						
A Toy for Two						
The Contest						
Helping Feet						
A Big Mistake						
Who Did It?						

Going Away

Characters

Julie Teller, 7 years old
John Teller, Julie's father
Ann Teller, Julie's mother
Uncle Jack and Aunt Helen Teller, Julie's uncle and aunt
King, Julie's dog, a German shepherd

Synopsis

The Teller family decides to take a vacation trip that will include a week of camping and riding inner tubes on the Chee-Caw River. Not being able to take Julie's dog King along poses a problem because Julie does not want the dog to stay in a kennel for a week. Julie's Uncle Jack and Aunt Helen solve the problem by offering to care for King while the family is away. King will have to spend only one night at the kennel.

Clues (10 items)

Letter to Julie from Aunt Helen and Uncle Jack

Hillside Kennel ad from the yellow pages

Note to Julie's mother from her father

List of "Things we need to take"

Ad for the Chee-Caw River Campground

Note from Julie to her mom

Picture of Julie hugging King

Postcard written by Julie to her aunt and uncle

Picture of the Teller family on the Chee-Caw River

Picture of Julie and King at the Hillside Kennel

Key Words

calm	downstream	river
campground	electricity	RVs
care	kennel	tube

Supporting Words

allowed	checkers	mosquito	vet
batteries	grooming	relax	volleyball
boarding	hiking	ruins	
canteen	located	tackle	
charcoal	mattresses	tennis	

Going Away

Discussion Questions

(Specific details)	1.	Tell me about the clues you have.
(Inference)	2.	Do any of the clues seem to go together?
(Classification)	3.	Can you put the clues together in two ways? For example, which group of clues could be called "Fun on the Trip"?

(Inference)	4.	What kind of trouble was the Teller family having?
		   a. How was Julie feeling when she was hugging King?
		   b. Who was Julie's father calling?
		   c. What can you find out from the letter that Aunt Helen and Uncle Jack sent to Julie?

(Sequence)	5.	Put the clues in the order that shows how you think things happened.
(Cause and effect)	6.	Why didn't Julie want King to go to the kennel for a week?
(Main idea)	7.	What is the main idea of this clues story? Make up another title for the story.

Follow-up

1. Write or tell a story about some kind of trouble a person had with a pet. Tell how the problem was solved. Draw a picture to go with the story.
2. What breed of dog was King? Find out more about King's breed and tell it to your class.
3. Make up a poem or song about another kind of pet. Share it with your class.
4. Look at the picture of Julie and King at the kennel. Talk about what kinds of work the girl does there. Then look at the ad about Hillside Kennel. It says, "Vet on call." What is a vet? What does "on call" mean?

Related Books

Iwasaki, Chihiro. *What's Fun Without a Friend?* New York: McGraw-Hill Book Co., 1975.

McCloskey, Robert. *Make Way for Ducklings.* New York: Viking Press, Inc., 1969.

Williams, Vera B. *Three Days on a River in a Red Canoe.* New York: Greenwillow Books, 1981.

Answer Key to Check-up Questions 1. **c** 2. **b** 3. **a** 4. **c** 5. **b** 6. **d**

Going Away

Check-up Questions

(Specific details) 1. Which words in the ad for Hillside Kennel tell you that animals which stay there are not left alone?
   a. Dog training
   b. Room to run
   c. 24-hour care
   d. Pet boarding

(Classification) 2. Which clues could be put in a group called "Finding a Place for King"?
   a. The list of "Things we need," and the picture of Julie hugging King
   b. The ad for Hillside Kennel, and the letter from Aunt Helen and Uncle Jack
   c. The ad for Chee-Caw River Campground, and the postcard from Julie
   d. The picture of the Teller family on the river, and the postcard from Julie

(Inference) 3. Pets were probably not allowed at Chee-Caw River Campground because
   a. they can bother other campers.
   b. they will run away.
   c. there wasn't enough room for them.
   d. most people do not like pets.

(Sequence) 4. Which one of these things happened **first** in the story?
   a. Julie wrote a postcard.
   b. Julie's father wrote a note to Julie's mother.
   c. The Teller family got the ad for the campground.
   d. King went to the kennel.

(Cause and effect) 5. Which of these clues probably made Julie very happy?
   a. The ad for the Hillside Kennel
   b. The letter from Aunt Helen and Uncle Jack
   c. Julie's note to her mother
   d. The picture of Julie at the kennel

(Main idea) 6. What is the main idea of this clues story?
   a. Some people like to ride in tubes.
   b. It is hard to take care of dogs.
   c. Campgrounds do not allow pets.
   d. Julie's family solved a pet problem.

The New Boy

Characters

Gary Wilson, 8 years old
Mrs. Carol Wilson, Gary's mother
Mrs. Podelski, Gary's teacher
Gary's classmates at Philip O. Brown Elementary School

Synopsis

Gary Wilson, a third grade boy, moves from his home on a dairy farm to an apartment in a large city. He enjoys city life, but he is very unhappy as the new boy at school because classmates tease him about his farm background. Classmates rapidly turn into friends, however, when Gary shows them how to construct a rabbit hutch which the class needs for its pet.

Clues (10 items)

Letter written by Mrs. Podelski to Gary's mother and father

Pages 8 and 9 from a book about rabbits

Thank-you letter written to Mr. Rand

Picture of Gary and the moving van at the dairy farm

Picture of Gary and the moving van at the apartment

Picture of Gary and his family caught in traffic

Picture of Gary looking down at the big city

Picture of Gary building the rabbit hutch

Drawing of a cow and a boy

Note written by Gary's mother, Carol, to her sister Jen

Key Words

apartment	fresh	pellets	rump
build	hutch	plant	shoulders
dairy farm	lift	rabbit	

Supporting Words

barley   loose   shady   sincerely

JUST CLUES: Experiences in Reading Comprehension   © 1985 Creative Publications

The New Boy

Discussion Questions

(Specific details)	1.	Tell me about the clues you have.
(Inference)	2.	Do any of the clues go together?
(Classification)	3.	Can you group the clues in two ways? For example, which group of clues could be called "Things About the Rabbit"?

(Inference)	4.	What was happening to Gary Wilson in this story?
		  a. Why would someone draw the cow picture?
		  b. How did the picture get torn?
		  c. Why did Gary come home crying?

(Sequence)	5.	Put the clues in the order that shows how you think things happened.
(Cause and effect)	6.	How did Gary's life on the farm help him in his new school?
(Main idea)	7.	What is the main idea of this clues story? Make up another title for the story.

Follow-up

1. Adopt a class pet. Read to find out how to build the right kind of home for your pet. Build the home. Find out what food and care your pet will need.
2. Pretend that you are Gary finding the drawing of the cow and boy. Tell how you feel about the picture.
3. Pretend that you have moved to a very different place from where you had been living. Write a story about what happens to you in your new school.
4. Draw a picture to show another way Gary's life on a dairy farm might help him or his new class.

Related Books

Dunn, Phoebe, and Judy Dunn. *The Animals of Buttercup Farm.* New York: Random House, Inc., 1981.

Gordon, Shirley. *Crystal Is the New Girl.* New York: Harper & Row, Inc., 1976.

Sharmat, Marjorie W. *Gila Monsters Meet You at the Airport.* New York: MacMillan Publishing Co., Inc., 1980.

Answer Key to Check-up Questions   1. d   2. a   3. c   4. c   5. b   6. a

The New Boy

(Specific details) 1. In the clue that tells you how to care for rabbits, which of these sentences tells you one way to get a rabbit cage?
   a. Be sure that the rabbit has lots of fresh air.
   b. A rabbit cage is called a *hutch*.
   c. Keep fresh water in the hutch all the time.
   d. You can also build one.

(Classification) 2. Which clues could be put in a group called "Things You Might See in a Big City"?
   a. The picture of Gary and his family in a car, and the picture of Gary looking down on the city
   b. The letter from Mrs. Podelski to Gary's mother and father, and the drawing of the cow
   c. The picture of the moving van at the apartment, and the picture of the moving van at the farm
   d. The picture of the moving van at the farm, and the picture of Gary building the hutch

(Inference) 3. Think about all the clues. When you read Mrs. Podelski's letter, you can guess that
   a. Gary will move back to the farm.
   b. Gary's father will visit the school.
   c. Gary will build a rabbit cage for Walter.
   d. children are teasing Gary because he came from a farm.

(Sequence) 4. Which of these things happened **last** in the story?
   a. Mrs. Wilson wrote a note.
   b. Gary moved away from the farm.
   c. Gary built a rabbit hutch.
   d. Mr. Rand gave a rabbit to the class.

(Cause and effect) 5. Which clue shows why the children stopped teasing Gary?
   a. The thank-you letter to Mr. Rand
   b. The picture of Gary building the rabbit hutch
   c. The drawing of the cow and boy
   d. Mrs. Podelski's letter

(Main idea) 6. What is the main idea of this clues story?
   a. Children can learn from one another.
   b. Rabbits make good classroom pets.
   c. It is fun to build a rabbit hutch.
   d. New students make many new friends at school.

Just You and Me

Characters

Marci Baker, 7 years old
Deanne Lewis, 8 years old, Marci's friend
Bernard Baker, 13 years old, Marci's brother
Mrs. Joan Baker, Marci's mother
Pelican Pete, a security officer at Oceans Aweigh

Synopsis

Marci Baker's mother and brother take her and her friend Deanne Lewis to visit Oceans Aweigh, a nautical theme park. The girls wander away from Bernard at a refreshment stand and find themselves lost. While trying to find Bernard, Marci falls and hurts her knee. The girls remember a sign they read about lost children, and they go to a special station that looks like a red boat. There a kindly security officer, Pelican Pete, cares for them until Mrs. Baker comes for them.

Clues (7 items)

Picture of Pelican Pete's note to boys and girls

Marci's story about her day at Oceans Aweigh

Deanne's drawing about her day at Oceans Aweigh

Picture of Bernard buying hot dogs

Picture of Pelican Pete holding someone's hand

Important note for parents

Letter written by Mrs. Baker to her mother

Key Words

arrows	guess	Oceans Aweigh	plan
boat	important	parents	scare(d)
dolphin	lost	Pelican Pete	special

Supporting Words

okay   refreshments

Just You and Me

Discussion Questions

(Specific details)   1.   Tell me about the clues you have.

(Inference)   2.   Do any of the clues go together?

(Classification)   3.   Can you group the clues in two ways? For example, which group of clues could be called "Telling About Oceans Aweigh"?

(Inference)   4.   What happened at Oceans Aweigh that day?
   a.   What can you find out about Marci and Deanne from reading Marci's story?
   b.   Which girl drew the picture showing Oceans Aweigh? How do you know?
   c.   How did Marci feel about her day at Oceans Aweigh?

(Sequence)   5.   Put the clues in the order that shows how you think things happened.

(Cause and effect)   6.   What did Mrs. Baker and Bernard do after they found out that the girls were missing?

(Main idea)   7.   What is the main idea of this clues story? Make up another title for the story.

Follow-up

1. Act out parts of the story. Pretend that you are:
   a. Bernard, when he found out that the girls were missing.
   b. Mrs. Baker, when she found the girls.
   c. Pelican Pete, when he first met the lost girls.
2. Pretend that you are Marci or Deanne. Write a thank-you letter to Pelican Pete.
3. Tell a story about another family that looks for and finds their lost child. Draw a picture to go with your story.
4. Tell what your own family's rules are for what to do if you are lost.

Related Books

Bograd, Larry. *Lost in the Store*. New York: MacMillan Publishing Co., Inc., 1981.

Carrick, Carol, and Donald Carrick. *The Highest Balloon on the Common*. New York: Greenwillow Books, 1977.

Lisker, Sonia O. *Lost*. New York: Harcourt Brace Jovanovich, Inc., 1975.

Parenteau, Shirley. *I'll Bet You Thought I Was Lost*. New York: Lothrop, Lee & Shepard Co., 1981.

Answer Key to Check-up Questions   1. **a**   2. **b**   3. **b**   4. **a**   5. **c**   6. **a**

Just You and Me

Check-up Questions

(Specific details)   1.   Which of the things shown in Deanne's drawing helped the girls find Mrs. Baker?
     a.   Pelican Pete and the red boat
     b.   Bernard buying hot dogs
     c.   The children in the small boats
     d.   The dolphins and the trainer

(Classification)   2.   Which clues could be put in a group called "What to Do if You Get Lost"?
     a.   Mrs. Baker's letter to her mother, and Pelican Pete's note to boys and girls
     b.   Pelican Pete's note to boys and girls, and the important note for parents
     c.   Mrs. Baker's letter to her mother, and Marci's story
     d.   The picture of Pelican Pete holding someone's hand, and Marci's story

(Inference)   3.   Think about all the clues. When you look at Marci's story and Deanne's drawing, you can guess that
     a.   Pelican Pete liked hot dogs.
     b.   the girls got home safely.
     c.   the girls did not like Oceans Aweigh.
     d.   there were ten dolphins at Oceans Aweigh.

(Sequence)   4.   Which of these things happened **last** in the story?
     a.   Deanne drew a picture.
     b.   Mrs. Baker went to the red boat.
     c.   Marci and Deanne got hot dogs.
     d.   Mrs. Baker read the note about planning a good place to meet if children get lost.

(Cause and effect)   5.   Which one of these clues would make Marci's mother very happy?
     a.   The letter that she wrote
     b.   The important note for parents
     c.   The picture of Pelican Pete holding Marci's hand
     d.   Marci's story

(Main idea)   6.   What is the main idea of this clues story?
     a.   Two girls get lost and are found at Oceans Aweigh.
     b.   Friends meet Pelican Pete at a big red boat.
     c.   Two girls write and draw about Oceans Aweigh.
     d.   A boy buys hot dogs for himself and his sister.

A Toy for Two

Characters

Jose Gomez, 7 years old
Carlos Gomez, 7 years old, Jose's twin
Maria Gomez, mother of Jose and Carlos
Manuel Gomez, father of Jose and Carlos
Grandma Gomez

Synopsis

For their birthday, Jose and Carlos each receive a surprise gift of ten dollars from their grandmother. Both boys want to buy remote-controlled cars, but they do not have enough money to buy two cars. They decide to pool their money and share one car. A problem ensues when they bring the toy home. They have difficulty sharing it. In time, the boys develop rules for play, which saves the toy and allows them both to have fun playing with it.

Clues (10 items)

Letter from Grandma Gomez to Jose and Carlos

Picture of Jose and Carlos in a toy store

Picture of Jose and Carlos fighting over a toy car

List of rules about sharing

Note from Manuel to Maria

Picture of Jose and Carlos with their father

Picture of Jose and Carlos running the car up a ramp

Picture of a broken remote-controlled car

Thank-you letter written by Jose and Carlos to their grandmother

Page from a story entitled "One for Two"

Key Words

chance	neat	share
control	ramp	shopping
excited	remote-controlled	wreck

Supporting Words

favorite   grabbed   record   special

JUST CLUES: Experiences in Reading Comprehension

A Toy for Two

Discussion Questions

(Specific details) 1. Tell me about the clues you have.

(Inference) 2. Do any of the clues go together? Which clue is **not** about Jose and Carlos? How does it fit in with the story?

(Classification) 3. Can you group the clues in two ways? For example, which group of clues could be called "No Sharing Here"?

(Inference) 4. What was happening between Jose and Carlos?
   a. Why did the boys decide to buy one toy instead of two?
   b. Who wrote "Ways to share our car"? Why do you think so?
   c. Was the toy ever taken away from the boys?

(Sequence) 5. Put the clues in the order that shows how you think things happened.

(Cause and effect) 6. How did the remote-controlled car get broken?

(Main idea) 7. What is the main idea of this clues story? Make up another title for the story.

Follow-up

1. Read the page from the "One for Two" story again. Write an ending for the story.
2. Pretend that you going to share a toy with a friend or with your brother or sister. Make up your own list of rules for sharing it. Tell what might happen if someone doesn't obey the rules.
3. Make up a short play about a time when you shared something you really liked with someone else. Act out the play with a friend or classmate.
4. On a tape recorder, tell a story about two children who are not sharing a toy very well. Pretend that you are both of the children. Use a different voice for each child. Play the tape for your classmates and have them guess what is happening.

Related Books

Beim, Lorraine, and Jerrold Beim. *Two Is a Team.* New York: Harcourt Brace Jovanovich, Inc., 1973.

Corey, Dorothy. *We All Share.* Chicago: Albert Whitman & Co., 1980.

Glovach, Linda. *Let's Make a Deal.* Englewood Cliffs, New Jersey: Prentice-Hall, Inc., 1975.

Answer Key to Check-up Questions 1. d 2. a 3. b 4. c 5. d 6. b

A Toy for Two

Check-up Questions

(Specific details)   1.   In the letter from Jose and Carlos to their grandmother, which sentence shows that the boys really liked their new toy?
- a.   Thank you for the money.
- b.   It broke, but Dad fixed it.
- c.   We had some fights about it.
- d.   It's the best toy we ever got!

(Classification)   2.   Which clues could be put in a group called "Sharing"?
- a.   The list of rules, and the picture of the boys with the car on the ramp
- b.   The letter from Grandma G., and the note from the boys' father to their mother
- c.   The picture of the boys with their father, and the page from the storybook
- d.   The boys' letter to their grandmother, and the picture of the broken car

(Inference)   3.   Which clue tells you that the boys probably obeyed the rules for sharing?
- a.   The picture of the boys with their father
- b.   The picture of the boys playing with the car on the ramp
- c.   The picture of the broken car
- d.   The picture of the boys in the toy store

(Sequence)   4.   Which of these things happened **first** in the story?
- a.   The remote-controlled car got broken.
- b.   The boys' father repaired the broken car.
- c.   The boys received a letter and money from their grandmother.
- d.   The boys made some rules for sharing their new toy.

(Cause and effect)   5.   Which one of these clues helped the boys learn how to share their new toy?
- a.   The letter from their grandmother
- b.   The note from their father
- c.   The picture of the boys in the toy store
- d.   The list of rules

(Main idea)   6.   What is the main idea of this clues story?
- a.   It is fun to play with a new toy.
- b.   When two boys learn how to share, they have fun with a new toy.
- c.   Buying one toy and sharing it is not a very good idea.
- d.   Toys often get broken when more than one person plays with them.

JUST CLUES: Experiences in Reading Comprehension   © 1985 Creative Publications

The Contest

Characters

Anita Perez, 9 years old
Luz Ruiz, 9 years old, Anita's friend

Synopsis

Anita Perez collects stickers, as does her friend Luz and most of the other girls she knows. They trade stickers and enjoy filling special books with their collections. When the girls learn that there is a sticker-design contest at a local store, they decide to enter it. Anita thinks of different ideas for stickers, but not one of them seems to please her. Then one night she dreams that she creates a giant sticker and that it falls on her. She awakens to find that a kitten poster on her wall has come loose and fallen on her. This experience gives her some terrific ideas for sticker designs. She enters the designs and wins the contest.

Clues (10 items)

Picture of the sign that tells about the sticker contest

Picture of Anita, Luz, and a friend trading stickers

Picture of the sign that names the contest winners

Picture of the First Prize

Contest entry form, showing a heart and a clown

Picture of kitten poster in Anita's bedroom

Picture of Anita waking up in her bed

Anita's drawing about her dream

Anita's letter to her granddaddy

Contest entry form, showing yarn and kittens

Key Words

collect	contest	kittens	sticker(s)
collection	designs	prize(s)	
congratulations	dream	rules	

Supporting Words

enter	mess	Saturday	tune
entry form	picture	tired	winners

The Contest

Discussion Questions

(Specific details)   1.   Tell me about the clues you have.

(Inference)   2.   Do any of the clues seem to go together?

(Classification)   3.   Can you group the clues in two ways? For example, which group of clues could be called "Getting in the Contest"?

(Inference)   4.   What was happening to Anita in this story?
   a.   What was the big sticker in Anita's dream?
   b.   Name two things that Anita liked a lot.
   c.   What do you think Anita did with the stickers that she won?

(Sequence)   5.   Put the clues in the order that shows how you think things happened.

(Cause and effect)   6.   Why did Anita write to her granddaddy?

(Main idea)   7.   What is the main idea of this clues story?

Follow-up

1.   Have a "Collection Day." You and your friends can bring your sticker collections to school and talk about them. You might also bring other kinds of collections, such as stamps, coins, and models. Talk about how you started your collections.
2.   Write or tell a story. Use one of these titles for it.
   "My Collection"
   "When I Was in a Contest"
3.   Draw a picture about a dream that you have had. Tell about the picture.
4.   Have a "Design-a-Sticker" contest in your classroom. Put the sticker designs on a bulletin board so that everybody can see them.

Related Books

Foreman, Michael. *Land of Dreams*. New York: Holt, Rinehart & Winston, Inc., 1982.
Hoban, Russell. *How Tom Beat Captain Najork and His Hired Sportsmen*. New York: Atheneum Pubs., 1975.
Keats, Ezra J. *Dreams*. New York: MacMillan Publishing Co., Inc., 1974.

Answer Key to Check-up Questions   1. **a**   2. **d**   3. **c**   4. **b**   5. **b**   6. **d**

The Contest

Check-up Questions

(Specific details) 1. Which of these words on the sticker contest sign do **not** give a rule of the contest?
    a. LOVE STICKERS?
    b. Children ages 7-10 may enter.
    c. Enter by May 5.
    d. Draw six sticker designs.

(Classification) 2. Which clues could be put in a group called "A Funny Dream"?
    a. Anita's letter to her granddaddy, and the picture that shows the contest rules
    b. The picture of the First Prize, and the picture of the sign that names the contest winners
    c. The picture of the kitten poster on the wall, and the picture of Anita waking up in bed
    d. The picture of Anita waking up in bed, and Anita's drawing

(Inference) 3. When you look at the contest entry form that shows a heart and a clown, you can guess that Anita
    a. liked to draw animals.
    b. did not like jokes.
    c. was not happy with these drawings.
    d. entered these sticker designs in the contest.

(Sequence) 4. Which of these things happened **first** in the story?
    a. The sign that named the contest winners was put up in the store window.
    b. Anita and her friends saw a sign with these words on it: "HERE'S YOUR BIG CHANCE!"
    c. Anita drew a picture about her dream.
    d. Anita and her friends read a sign with this word on it: "CONGRATULATIONS!"

(Cause and effect) 5. Which clue could tell you where Anita got her ideas for the winning sticker designs?
    a. The picture of the First Prize
    b. Anita's drawing about her dream
    c. The picture of the sign that named the contest winners
    d. The entry form that showed the heart and the clown

(Main idea) 6. What is the main idea of this clues story?
    a. Three girls had fun collecting stickers.
    b. It is easy to win contests.
    c. Kittens do funny things.
    d. Anita's dream helped her win a contest.

Helping Feet

Characters

Tanya Williams, 8 years old
Johnny Deer, 7 years old, Tanya's classmate
Betty James, 8 years old, Tanya's classmate

Mrs. James, Betty's mother
Mr. James, Betty's father
Mr. Long, the children's teacher

Synopsis

Betty James, a girl in Tanya Williams' and Johnny Deer's third grade class, has been injured in a car accident. She will recover, but there are many bills to be paid and her family is having trouble doing so. Every class at Oakdale Elementary, Betty's school, is doing something to make money to help her. Johnny Deer organizes a sponsored run-a-thon. On the day of the event, however, a storm changes the plans. The children and their teacher figure out a way to hold the fund-raiser anyway. Tanya suggests they hold it indoors on a course equal to the one planned for outside. The fund-raiser, now a walk-a-thon, takes more time, but the class has fun. It succeeds in raising enough money to buy Betty a wheelchair so that she can return to school.

Clues (11 items)

Newspaper report about Betty

Newspaper report about weather

Picture of the run-a-thon poster

Tanya's run-a-thon sponsor sheet

Get-well card written to Betty by her classmates

Thank-you letter written by Betty and her parents

Picture of Tanya and Johnny measuring the hall

Picture of run-a-thon and walk-a-thon maps

Picture of Betty James coming to Room 21 in a wheelchair

Picture of the children in Room 21 looking at the rain

Bill for the wheelchair

Key Words

accident	medical	run-a-thon
fund-raiser	/(per)	sponsor
lap	pledged	weather

Supporting Words

amount	injured	supply
bills	owed	thunderstorm
classmates	parents	wheelchair

 JUST CLUES: Experiences in Reading Comprehension

Helping Feet

Discussion Questions

(Specific details) 1. Tell me about the clues you have.

(Inference) 2. Do any of the clues go together?

(Classification) 3. Can you group the clues in two ways? For example, which group of clues could be called "Run-a-thon Problems"?

(Inference) 4. What was happening in Room 21?
   a. How did the class in Room 21 think it would surprise Mr. and Mrs. James and Betty?
   b. What does the thank-you letter tell you?
   c. What can you tell about Betty James from the picture of her coming into class?

(Sequence) 5. Put the clues in the order that shows how you think things happened.

(Cause and effect) 6. What did Betty and her parents do after they found out about the surprise?

(Main idea) 7. What is the main idea of this clues story? Make up another title for the story.

Follow-up

1. Look at Tanya's run-a-thon sponsor sheet. Pretend that each of the other 22 children in her class made at least that much money for Betty. How much money did Room 21 give Betty? If there were 10 more rooms in Oakdale Elementary School, and if each room raised as much money as Room 21 did, how much money did the school give to Betty?
2. Draw a picture that shows one of these parts of the story:
   a. The children holding the walk-a-thon indoors
   b. Betty getting the surprise gift from her friends
   c. The children in Room 21 welcoming Betty back and enjoying the surprise she brought
3. Write a story about one of these ideas:
   a. The first time Betty **walked** into Room 21 after her accident
   b. How rain can change plans
4. If you have helped raise money for someone who needed it, tell about your fund-raiser.

Related Books

Aardema, Verna. *Bringing the Rain to Kapiti Plain*. New York: Dial Press, 1981.
Hazen, Barbara S. *It's a Shame about the Rain: The Brighter Side of Disappointment*. New York: Human Sciences Press, Inc., 1982.
Herold, Ann B. *The Helping Day*. New York: Coward, McCann & Geoghegan, Inc., 1980.

Answer Key to Check-up Questions 1. b 2. c 3. a 4. d 5. b 6. d

Helping Feet

Check-up Questions

(Specific details) 1. In the newspaper report about Betty, which sentence tells **two** ways in which Oakdale Elementary School was raising money to help Betty?
   a. Call the school to find out how to help.
   b. Classes are holding bake sales and car washes.
   c. Betty's own third-grade class is holding a run-a-thon on the playground Friday.
   d. Do you want to help Betty?

(Classification) 2. Which clues could be put in a group called "Saying Thank You"?
   a. The bill for the wheelchair, and the picture of the two maps
   b. The picture of Betty coming to Room 21, and the picture of the run-a-thon poster
   c. The letter from Mr. and Mrs. James and Betty, and the picture of Betty coming to Room 21
   d. The newspaper report about Betty, and the newspaper report about the weather

(Inference) 3. Look at the get-well card and the letter from Mrs. and Mrs. James and Betty. What do you think the words "BIG SURPRISE" mean in each of these clues?
   a. The money raised in the walk-a-thon
   b. The number of laps walked by the children
   c. The news that the class will visit Betty
   d. The news that the children had learned to use a yardstick

(Sequence) 4. Which of these things happened **first** in the story?
   a. Betty visited her class at school.
   b. Johnny put the run-a-thon poster on the board.
   c. The children looked out the window at the rain.
   d. Johnny thought of a run-a-thon as a way to get money for Betty.

(Cause and effect) 5. Which one of these clues shows what happened because of the rain?
   a. The bill for the wheelchair
   b. The picture of the two maps
   c. The picture of the run-a-thon poster
   d. Tanya's run-a-thon sponsor sheet

(Main idea) 6. What is the main idea of this clues story?
   a. Children do not like rainy days.
   b. People often say thank you.
   c. A run-a-thon can be used to make money.
   d. Children can find many ways to help people.

 JUST CLUES: Experiences in Reading Comprehension   © 1985 Creative Publications

A Big Mistake

Characters

Ron Green, 9 years old
Ryan Green, 8 years old, Ron's brother
Janice Green, mother of Ron and Ryan
Kevin Green, father of Ron and Ryan
Mr. and Mrs. Walker, elderly neighbors of the Greens
Mrs. Elizabeth Jones, principal of the school that the Green boys attend

Synopsis

Ron and Ryan Green often play catch with their friends in the Greens' backyard. Their games are usually loud and lively, and disturb their nextdoor neighbors, the Walkers. When Mr. Walker complains about the noise, Ron and Ryan think he is mean. One day during play, Ron throws a ball and breaks the Walkers' kitchen window. When the boys' father takes them to the Walkers' house to apologize, the boys discover that Mr. Walker is not mean at all. He shares his collection of model trains with the boys. From then on, the boys play their most lively and noisy games at the school playground.

Clues (11 items)

Picture of Mr. Walker talking with Ron, Ryan, and other children

Note written by Mr. Walker to Mr. and Mrs. Green

Picture of broken window

Thank-you letter written by Mrs. Jones to the Walkers

Picture of Ron and Ryan playing with Mr. Walker's trains

Note written by Ron and Ryan to Mr. and Mrs. Walker

Picture of Ron, Ryan, and other children playing catch in the Greens' backyard

Note written by the boys' father to their mother

Story written by Ryan

Drawing of Mr. Walker

Picture of Ron, Ryan, and other children playing baseball on a school playground

Key Words

apologize   bothers   gift   mean   noise
bases   equipment grouch   neighbor

Supporting Words

sincerely   surprised

A Big Mistake

Discussion Questions

(Specific details) 1. Tell me about the clues you have.

(Inference) 2. Do any of the clues go together?

(Classification) 3. Can you group the clues in two ways? For example, which group of clues could be called "Making New Friends Is Fun"?

(Inference) 4. What was happening to Ron and Ryan?
  a. What did Mr. Walker want the boys to do when he wrote the note to their parents?
  b. What does the letter from Mrs. Jones tell you about the Walkers?
  c. Who drew the picture of Mr. Walker? Why?

(Sequence) 5. Put the clues in the order that shows how you think things happened.

(Cause and effect) 6. What caused Ron and Ryan to change the way they felt about Mr. Walker?

(Main idea) 7. What is the main idea of this clues story? Make up another title for the story.

Follow-up

1. With four of your classmates, act out the part of the story in which Ron, Ryan, and their father go over to apologize to the Walkers.
2. Make a bulletin board with the title "Making New Friends." Use drawings, magazine pictures, and photographs to show how friends get together to do things. Show some friends who are not the same age.
3. Make a list of activities and games that are fun for boys and girls. With your classmates, decide which ones you could play and could not play in the Greens' backyard. Tell why you make each choice.
4. Write a story about some ways that boys and girls and older people can enjoy doing things together.

Related Books

Herda, D.J. *Model Railroads*. New York: Franklin Watts, Inc., 1982.
Miles, Miska. *Annie and the Old One*. Boston: Little, Brown & Co., 1971.
Politi, Leo. *Mr. Fong's Toy Shop*. New York: Charles Scribner's Sons, 1978.

Answer Key to Check-up Questions   1. **c**   2. **a**   3. **d**   4. **c**   5. **d**   6. **b**

A Big Mistake

Check-up Questions

(Specific details)   1. In the letter from Mrs. Jones to Mr. and Mrs. Walker, which sentence tells what the school will do with the gift from the Walkers?
   a. Dear Mr. and Mrs. Walker:
   b. We were surprised to find out that you went to our school when you were young.
   c. We will use the money to buy new baseballs, bats, and bases.
   d. We always need new equipment for our playground.

(Classification)   2. Which clues could be put in a group called "Not Happy"?
   a. The picture of Mr. Walker and the children in the backyard, and the picture of Ron and Ryan with the broken window
   b. The picture of Ron and Ryan playing with the trains, and the picture of the children playing on the playground
   c. The note to Mr. and Mrs. Green from Mr. Walker, and the letter written by Mrs. Jones
   d. The note from Ron and Ryan to Mr. and Mrs. Walker, and the drawing of Mr. Walker

(Inference)   3. From the letter written by Mrs. Jones, you can tell that Mr. and Mrs. Walker
   a. didn't like children.
   b. liked model trains.
   c. were angry.
   d. liked to help children.

(Sequence)   4. Which of these clues tells what happened **last** in the story?
   a. The picture of the boys with the broken window
   b. The note written by Ron and Ryan to the Walkers
   c. Ryan's story, "Making Friends"
   d. The drawing of Mr. Walker

(Cause and effect)   5. What happened because the boys and their father visited the Walkers' house?
   a. The boys decided to buy a model train set.
   b. The boys' father wrote a note to their mother.
   c. Ron broke a window.
   d. Ron and Ryan found out that they were wrong about Mr. Walker.

(Main idea)   6. What is the main idea of this clues story?
   a. You can have fun running model trains.
   b. Neighbors can learn to understand each other.
   c. People do not like loud noises.
   d. Baseballs can break windows.

Who Did It?

Characters

Tim Barry, 8 years old
Patty Ling, 8 years old, Tim's neighbor and friend
Mrs. Barry, Tim's mother
Mr. Brown, a neighbor of Patty Ling and the Barry family

Synopsis

Tim Barry and Patty Ling live on Blue Lake Road near an undeveloped, wooded area. When Mrs. Barry and Tim are in Yellowstone National Park on vacation, someone gets into their house and makes a terrible mess. When Tim returns home, he and Patty play detective. They find out that the intruder was actually a raccoon.

Clues (8 items)

Animal card about raccoons

Animal card about opossums

Letter from Mr. Brown to Mrs. Barry

Picture of children's hands holding animal cards

Postcard from Mrs. Barry to Mr. Brown

Letter from Patty Ling to Tim

Picture of a mess on the porch of the Barry home

Picture of a mess in the kitchen of the Barry home

Key Words

animal	danger	mess	pointed
bushy	enemy	neighbor	raccoon
climbers	fur	opossum	ringtail
curious	hind	plump	tracks

Supporting Words

dead	hisses	snails	thumb
eastern	jars	snakes	United States
favorite	mushrooms	stripes	west coast
garbage	persimmon	swamps	

Who Did It?

Discussion Questions

(Specific details)   1.   Tell me about the clues you have.

(Inference)   2.   Do any of the clues go together?

(Classification)   3.   Can you group the clues in two ways? For example, which group of clues could be called "Finding Out About the Mess"?

(Inference)   4.   What was happening in this story?
- a. Who do you think was looking at the animal cards?
- b. Who took the picture of the mess on the porch? How do you know?
- c. What can you find out by looking at the picture of the tracks in the kitchen?

(Sequence)   5.   Put the clues in the order that shows how you think things happened.

(Cause and effect)   6.   Why did Patty Ling write a letter to Tim?

(Main idea)   7.   What is the main idea of this clues story?

Follow-up

1. Draw, tell, or write the whole story about the trouble at the house on Blue Lake Road. You may want to do all three.
2. Read a book about a raccoon. Tell how the raccoon in the book is like the one in this story.
3. Pretend that you are Patty or Tim looking at the animal cards and the pictures of the mess. Tell what you find out.
4. Make up a song about raccoons. Teach it to your class. Write the words and draw a picture to go with the words.

Related Books

Bourne, Miriam A. *Raccoons Are for Loving.* New York: Random House, Inc., 1968.
Kellogg, Steven. *The Mystery of the Missing Red Mitten.* New York: Dial Press, 1974.
Miklowitz, Gloria D. *Save That Raccoon!* New York: Harcourt Brace Jovanovich, Inc., 1978.

Answer Key to Check-up Questions   1. d   2. c   3. d   4. b   5. a   6. c

Who Did It?

Check-up Questions

(Specific details)   1. Which part of the animal cards helped Patty and Tim the most as they tried to find out who made the mess?
   a. The pictures of the animals
   b. The colors of the animals
   c. The words that told about where the animals live
   d. The pictures of the animal tracks

(Classification)   2. Which clues could be put in a group called "Checking the Clues"?
   a. The letter from Mr. Brown, and the postcard from Mrs. Barry
   b. The picture of the hands holding animal cards, and the postcard from Mrs. Barry
   c. The picture of the animal tracks in the kitchen, and the picture of the hands holding animal cards
   d. The letter from Mr. Brown, and the letter from Patty Ling

(Inference)   3. When you read Patty's letter, you can guess that she
   a. had just seen a raccoon.
   b. knew which raccoon had made the mess.
   c. had a pet raccoon.
   d. was not sure what had made the mess.

(Sequence)   4. Which of these things happened **first** in the story?
   a. Tim and Patty looked at the animal cards.
   b. Mr. Brown took a picture of the mess on the porch.
   c. Mrs. Barry wrote a postcard to Mr. Brown.
   d. Tim and Patty saw the mess in the kitchen.

(Cause and effect)   5. Mr. Brown found the mess because
   a. his dog, Rex, ran around the back of Tim's house.
   b. he got a postcard from Mrs. Barry.
   c. Patty Ling told him about it.
   d. he saw someone in the house.

(Main idea)   6. What is the main idea of this clues story?
   a. A family lives in a home on Blue Lake Road.
   b. There is much to learn about animals.
   c. Children find out that a raccoon made a mess.
   d. Raccoons eat fish and fruit.

   JUST CLUES: Experiences in Reading Comprehension

Index to Clues

The New Boy

Philip O. Brown Elementary School

September 21, 1984

Mr. and Mrs. William Wilson
Twin Oaks Apartments, #24
1201 Twin Oaks Road
Silver City, TX 78228

Dear Mr. and Mrs. Wilson:

Thank you for your visit and note. Yes, I think Mr. Wilson's idea is a good one. Gary can go ahead with his plan right away. He can bring the wire in Monday and start.

I know Gary thinks it is funny that we do not know how to do it. I know that what Gary is doing will be good for the class. It will also be good for Gary.

Sincerely,

Anna Podelski

Mrs. Podelski
Teacher

THE BODY OF A RABBIT

ear

shoulders

tail

rump

leg

foot

PET RABBITS

How to Lift a Rabbit

With one hand, take hold of the loose skin on the back of the rabbit, over its shoulders. Place your other hand under its rump, and lift.

How to Care for a Rabbit

Its Cage

A rabbit cage is called a *hutch*. You can buy a hutch from a pet store. You can also build one.

Put the hutch in a shady place, off the ground. Be sure that the rabbit has lots of fresh air. Keep it warm and dry. Use hay or straw for the rabbit's bed. Clean the hutch every day.

Food and Water

Keep fresh water in the hutch all the time. Feed the rabbit such things as wheat, oats, and barley. You can buy this food in *pellets* from a pet store. Rabbits also like grass, turnips, carrots, and beets. Do not give a rabbit too much food. Give it only as much food as it can eat in one half hour.

The New Boy

The New Boy

September 19, 1984

Dear Jen,

    We miss you. Gary is always talking about Aunt Jen on the farm.

    Yes, the moving van got here. All our things are out of the boxes. Now we have to put them away.

    Life in the apartment is not the same as on the farm. We do not have as much room.

    Bill likes his new job at the plant. Gary likes the city, but not the new school. Yesterday he came home crying. He did not want to talk about it. Tomorrow I will see his teacher.

    I will write more soon.

                  Love,

                  Carol,
                  your big-city sister

Dear Jose and Carlos,

Happy birthday, boys. Only three more days until your birthday. I'll bet you are both excited.

Here is $10 for each of you. You may each buy something that you really want. Have fun shopping.

Love,
Grandma G.

MARIA,
THE BOYS WERE AT IT AGAIN BEFORE SCHOOL. I'M TIRED OF THEIR FIGHTING. THEY CAN'T SEEM TO LEARN HOW TO SHARE. I WILL TAKE IT AWAY FROM THEM IF THIS HAPPENS ONCE MORE. I TOLD THEM THAT TODAY WAS THEIR LAST CHANCE. WE'LL TALK ABOUT IT AFTER WORK.

MANUEL

A Toy for Two

A Toy for Two

Helping Feet

"Run for Betty" Run-a-Thon

Sponsor Sheet

Hi! My name is **Tanya Williams** .

On Friday I will run at school to get money for Betty James' bills. Please help me.

I will try to run **25** laps.

SPONSOR	AMOUNT PLEDGED	NUMBER OF LAPS	AMOUNT OWED
1. Mrs. Ruby Williams	10¢/lap	25	$ 2.50
2. Mr. John Williams	10¢/lap	25	2.50
3. Rhonda Brown	5¢/lap	25	1.25
4. Mrs. Bell	1¢/lap	25	.25
5. JOE GREEN	5¢/LAP	25	1.25
6. Grandma Williams	10¢/Lap	25	2.50
7. Billy Brown	75¢ total	25	.75
8. Aunt Sue	50¢/lap	25	12.50
9. Mrs. Jones	25¢/lap	25	6.25
10. Mary Winter	10¢/lap	25	2.50

TOTAL: $ **32.25**

THANK YOU from Betty and me. I ran **25** laps!

Tanya Williams
Runner

Mr. Long
Teacher

36

OAKDALE MEDICAL SUPPLY COMPANY
774 Main Street, Oakdale
312-3233

SOLD TO:

DATE:

Mr. Jerry James
411 West 4th Street
Oakdale

October 3, 1984

1 child's wheelchair (size 9-12 years) $475.00

PAID

Check # 756

picked up 10/3/84

Helping Feet

Helping Feet

A Big Mistake

Washington Elementary School

179 East Pelt Road   New Rock, New York 10805

September 21, 1984

Mr. and Mrs. James Walker
241 Rose Street
New Rock, New York 10805

Dear Mr. and Mrs. Walker:

Thank you so much for the gift. We will use the money to buy new baseballs, bats, and bases. We always need new equipment for our playground.

We were surprised to find out that you went to our school when you were young. Thank you again for helping the boys and girls who go to the school now.

Sincerely,

Elizabeth Jones

Mrs. Elizabeth Jones
Principal

Dear Mom,
I know what you say but
I want him to go with
us. ~~It is~~ I know he
will not like that
place for a week.
                    Love,
                    Julie

Things we need to take

food for one week
water canteen
sun hat
snack food
pots and pans
swimsuits
hiking shoes
tennis shoes
snakebite kit
air mattresses
sleeping bags
gas lamp
matches
ice
ice chest
folding table
trash bags
mosquito stuff
flashlight and batteries

tent
toolbox
fishing tackle
raincoats
charcoal

volleyball
checkers
game

Going Away

Going Away

Going Away

Going Away

Going Away

Going Away

Going Away

We know you can't take him with you. We would love to take care of him. The only trouble is that we can't pick him up until Saturday afternoon. Can King stay at the kennel for one night?

Give us a call.

Love,

Aunt Helen and Uncle Jack

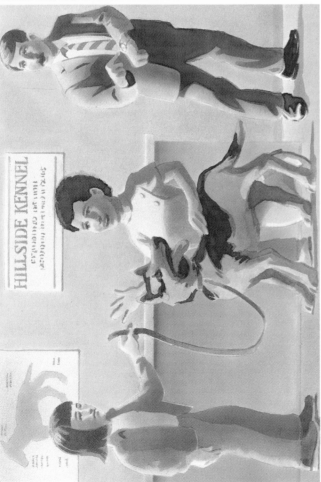

ANN,
I'LL BE HOME AT 5. HAVE EVERYTHING READY TO GO. MY FISHING TACKLE BOX IS ON THE SHELF. I'LL DROP KING OFF BEFORE DINNER. TELL JULIE TO BE READY.

JOHN

HILLSIDE KENNEL

- Pet boarding
- Pet grooming
- Dog training
- Room to run
- 24-hour care
- Vet on call

 538-4770

814 Willow Road   Oakwood

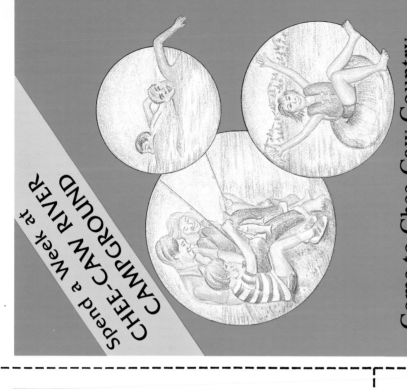

SPEND a Week at
CHEE-CAW RIVER
CAMPGROUND

Come to Chee-Caw Country

Camp on the banks of the Chee-Caw River. Ride a tube downstream for six miles. Enjoy the pretty Pine Mountains. Catch fish for your supper.

SPECIAL TREATS! Ride the calm waters of the river and swim in Hidden Creek. See the Indian ruins at Blue Canyon.

Bring the whole family. Relax and enjoy the quiet. RVs are welcome. Sorry, no electricity. Pets not allowed.

Campground is located 35 miles north of River Bend City off Highway 67.

USA 13¢

Post Card

Mr. and Mrs. Jack Teller
138 West Story Road
Highwater, WI
53140

Distributed by Creative Publications

Chee-Caw River Campground

Dear Aunt Helen and Uncle Jack,

We are having lots of fun. I was in the tube with Daddy this morning. The water was cold. FUN! FUN! Give King a big hug for me. We will see you on Sunday.

XXX Love, Julie OOO

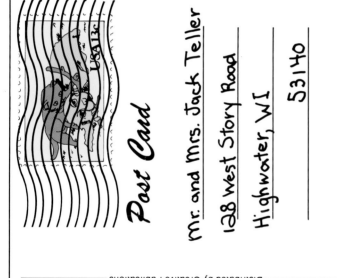

Going Away

Going Away

Going Away

46

The New Boy

The New Boy

The New Boy

The New Boy

47

September 10, 1984

Dear Mr. Rand,
   Thank you for the rabbit. We named
him Walter. We will take good care of him.
   Walter lives in a box in our room.
He can't see out of it. We want to make
a good house for him. We will find out
how to do it.
   Thank you again.

                    Your friends from
                    Mrs. Podelski's third grade,

Rosa   Casey   Katie   Joey
Robert   Tonda   Delanna   Sean
Ellen   Rena   Nathan   Mike
Johnny   Kenyon   Juan   Ann
Terri   John   Scott   Craig
Mary   Brad   Susan   Krissy

The New Boy

The New Boy

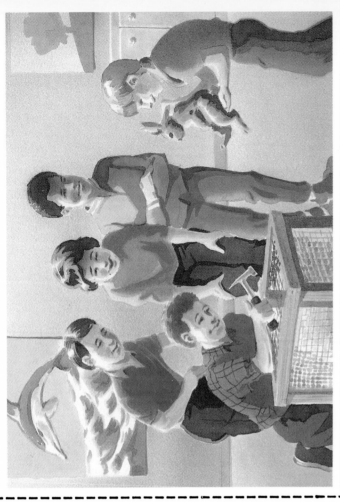

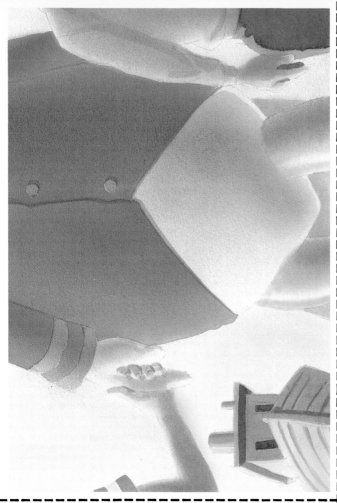

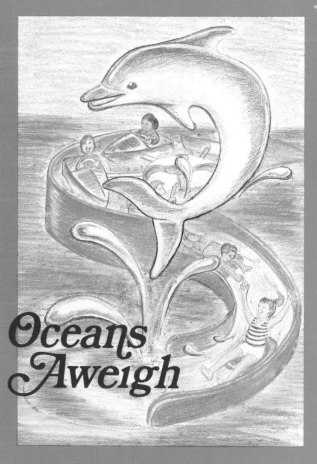

Oceans Aweigh

Important Note for Parents

Oceans Aweigh is a big place. Sometimes children get lost here.

Right now, make a plan with your child. Tell your child to stay close to you.

Tell your child to follow the red arrows to the big red boat if he or she gets lost. There, one of our workers, named Pelican Pete, will wait with your child until you come.

Be sure that your child **can** and **will** say his or her name.

Right now, please talk about this with your child. Help us make Oceans Aweigh even more fun!

Just You and Me

Just You and Me

Just You and Me

Just You and Me

Just You and Me

BOYS AND GIRLS!
If you get lost,
come to the big
red boat.
I will help you
find your family.
Your friend,
Pelican Pete
← Red Boat

ENTER

July 10, 1984

Dear Mom,

Marci and her friend Deanne gave us a real
scare today! Bernard and I took them to Ocea
Aweigh. He went with the girls to buy hot do
The girls walked off alone to see the dolp
Bernard couldn't find them. We looked ev
for them. You can guess how scared I was
last, they came to a special place in t
that we had talked about. We found the
I had a long talk with both girls abo
with us. After all that, the four of

Love,

Joan

P.S. I was really angry at firs
everything is okay.

From:
J. Baker
1670 N. Pueblo
Burlingame, Ca
94010

SAN FRANCISCO CA
PM

56

mrs. Baker

marci

Bernard

Deanne

Marci Baker

My Day at Oceans Aweigh

I went to Oceans Aweigh. My mother and brother and Deanne went too. At first it was fun. Then guess what Deanne and I did. It was not fun!

Just You and Me

Just You and Me

58

A Toy for Two

A Toy for Two

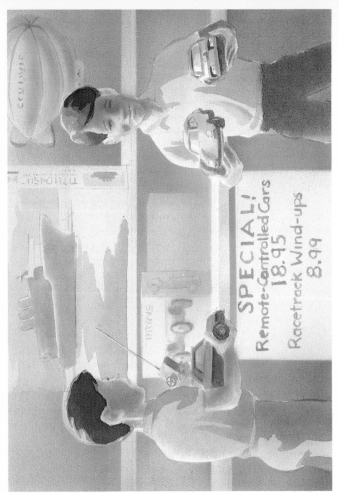

SPECIAL!
Remote-Controlled Cars
18.95
Racetrack Wind-ups
8.99

Dear Grandma G.,

Thank you for the money. We put our money together and bought a neat remote-controlled car.

We had some fights about it. It broke, but Dad fixed it. It works okay now. Dad helped us plan how to share it. We even made a ramp for it. It's the best toy we ever got!

Thank you a lot!

Love,
Jose and Carlos

60

Ways to share our car

Only one on control at a time.
Carlos gets to run it alone on Saturday.
Jose gets to run it alone on Sunday.
Don't fight about the car.
Don't wreck the car.
Plan how to share it.

A Toy for Two

A Toy for Two

A Toy for Two

A Toy for Two

A Toy for Two

Beth took out her favorite record and put it on the record player.

"I'm going to play mine first," said Karen.

"No you're not!" yelled Beth.

"I got here first!"

"It's mine, too," shouted Karen. "You can play your record after mine."

Both girls grabbed for the arm of the record player. Just then, the

The Contest

The Contest

The Contest

The Contest

The Contest

The Contest

The Contest

Dear Granddaddy,

You will like this letter. You know how I like stickers. The toy store had a sticker contest. I made up six stickers. I won the contest! Look at the picture inside to see what I won.

Love,

Anita xxx ooo

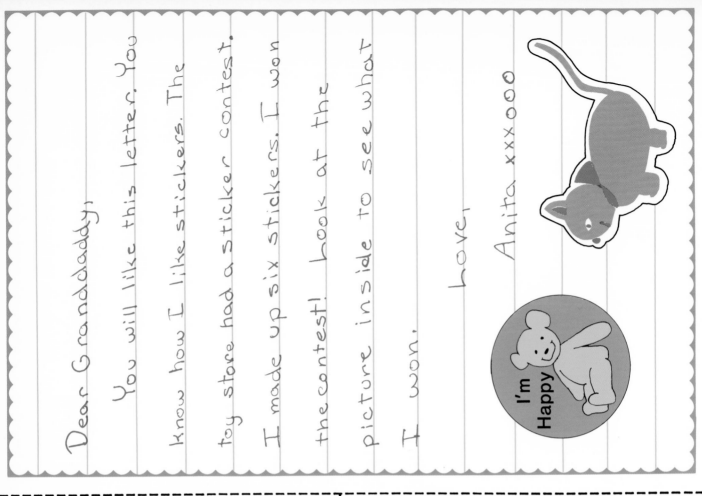

I'm Happy

GOLDMAN'S TOYS

LOVE STICKERS? HERE'S YOUR BIG CHANCE!

STICKER CONTEST

<u>Rules</u>
- Children ages 7–10 may enter.
- Use contest entry form.
- Draw six sticker designs.
- Enter by May 5.

Big sticker prizes for the best designs!

Get contest entry forms from Mr. and Mrs. Goldman.

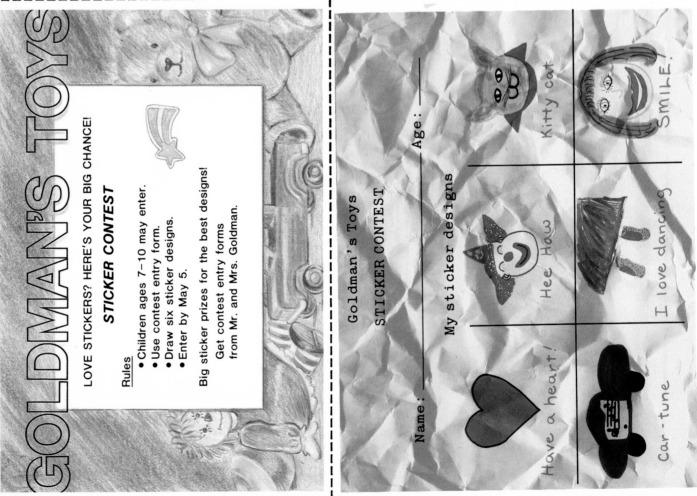

Goldman's Toys

STICKER CONTEST

Name : _____

Age : _____

My sticker designs

Kitty cat

Hee Haw

Have a heart!

Car-tune

I love dancing

SMILE!

My Funny Dream

Anita Perez

Yarn	Kitten	Kitten and yarn
	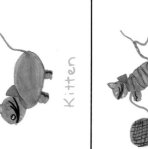	Tired kitty
Yarn and Kitten	A Mess!	

The Contest

The Contest

The Contest

Helping Feet

HELPING FEET

Dear Betty,
Get well soon!

We miss you!

We have a BIG SURPRISE
for you.

We will surprise your
mother and father too.

Love,
Your friends in
Room 21

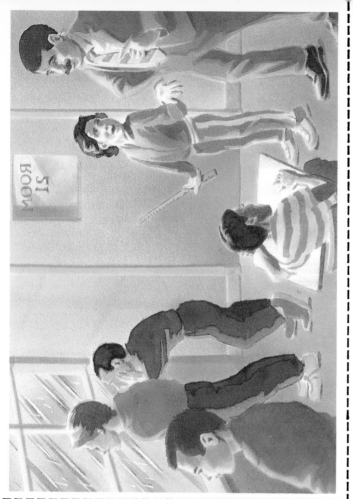

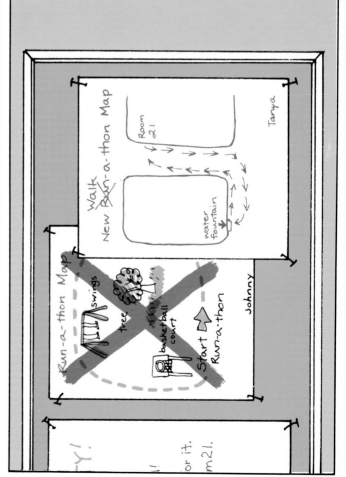

73

Helping Feet

Helping Feet

Helping Feet

Helping Feet

74

Helping Feet

Helping Feet

Helping Feet

75

TODAY'S WEATHER

There will be a surprise change in weather today. Expect heavy rains, strong winds, and thunderstorm by late morning. Sunny skies will be back on Saturday.

★ ★ ★ Friday, September 28, 1984

WS

Girl Gets Better, But Help Is Needed

Oakdale—Friends and family of Betty James are pleased to say that she is getting better. Betty, a lively 7-year-old, was injured in a car accident on Miller Road on Saturday.

While Betty is getting well, the bills keep getting bigger. Betty's parents cannot pay all of the bills because Mr. James is out of work right now.

Betty's school, Oakdale Elementary, is helping the James family. Classes are holding bake sales and car washes to raise money. Betty's own third-grade class is holding a run-a-thon on the playground Friday.

Do you want to help Betty? Call the school at 411-1112 to find out how you can help. Betty needs YOU!

Dear Tanya, Johnny, and all the children in Room 21,

THANK YOU for your BIG SURPRISE! We can not get over it.

Yes, you do have VERY helpful feet! Betty is lucky to have good friends like you.

Next Monday you will see Betty. You will see how we used the surprise too.

Thanks very much again.

Love,

Mr. & Mrs. James

P.S. I am saying thank you too. Love, Betty

76

Ryan Green
Grade 3

Making Friends

Last week we got some new friends. They live next door to us. We used to think Mr. Walker was mean. We were not right. He is very nice. So is Mrs. Walker. We just didn't know that. Now we are friends with Mr. and Mrs. Walker.

Janice,
   Ron broke the Walker's window. He and Ryan were playing ball in the backyard again. We have gone next door to apologize and to see about fixing it. We'll be home in a little while.

   Kevin

A Big Mistake

A Big Mistake

A Big Mistake

A Big Mistake

A Big Mistake

A Big Mistake

A Big Mistake

Dear Mr. and Mrs. Green,

    Your boys and their friends are making too much noise near our house. I don't want to be a grouch, but it often bothers Mrs. Walker and me. Will you please talk with them?
    Thank you.

                    Your neighbor,

                    Mr. Walker

Dear Mr. and Mrs. Walker,
    We are sorry about the window. We are sorry that you had to clean up the glass. We are paying for the glass when Dad fixes your window tomorrow. Thank you for showing us your trains. That was fun.
                Your friends,
                Ryan   Ron

Mean Mr. W

A Big Mistake

A Big Mistake

A Big Mistake

82

Who Did It?

Who Did It?

Who Did It?

Who Did It?

Who Did It?

Who Did It?

Who Did It?

Who Did It?

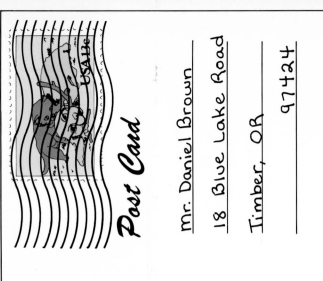

Post Card

USA 14c

Mr. Daniel Brown
18 Blue Lake Road
Timber, OR   97424

Dear Mr. Brown,
   What a mess! Thank you
for closing the screendoor.
I wonder how it happened.
   Tim received a note
about it from Patty Ling.
She wants to work on the
case to find out who did it.
Thanks for the picture.

        Your neighbor,
         Mrs. Barry

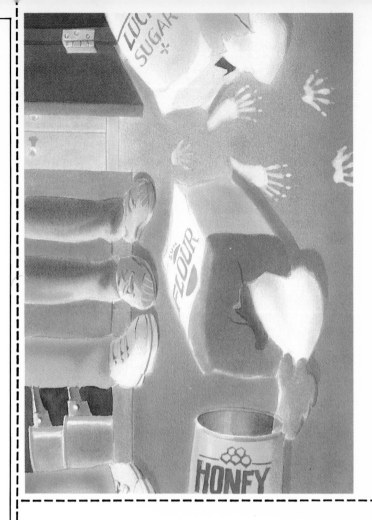

July 8, 1984

Dear Mrs. Barry,

   This morning Rex started barking
when I was walking him past your house.
He ran around to the back of your house
and I followed him. Your back screendoor was open and there was a big mess
on the porch!

   I looked around but could not find
anyone. The door into the house was
still locked. I shut the screendoor to
the porch.

   I am glad that you will be home on
Friday.

        Your neighbor,
         Mr. Brown